Ages **4+**

Let's Practice

Addition & Subtraction

Contents

Brighter Child®
An imprint of Carson Dellosa Education
PO Box 35665
Greensboro, NC 27425 USA

Printed in the USA • All rights reserved.   ISBN 978-1-4838-4604-0
11-263211151

Add 0

Trace and write to solve the problems.

$2 + 0 =$

2

$4 + 0 =$

4

+0

$6 + 0 =$

6 N D

$8 + 0 =$

8

Trace and color the shapes. Then, draw and color your own shape.

Add 1

Trace and write to solve the problems.

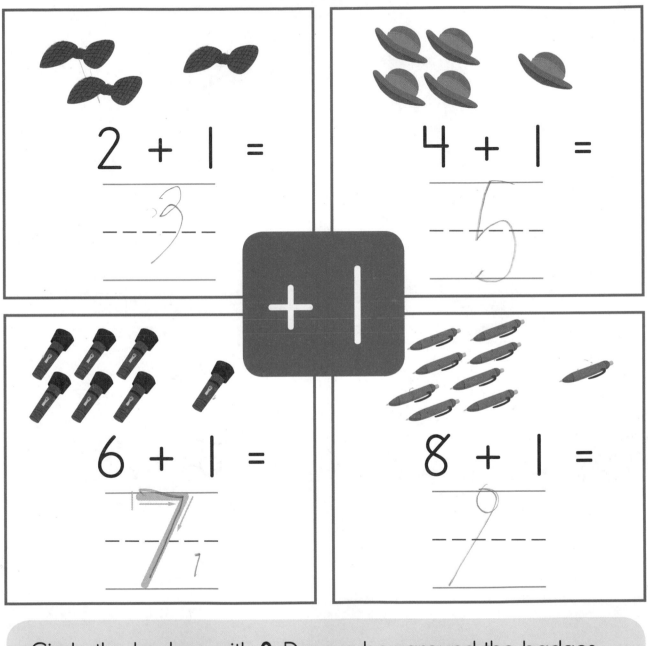

2 + 1 =
3

4 + 1 =
5

+ 1

6 + 1 =
7

8 + 1 =
9

Circle the badges with **0**. Draw a box around the badges with **1**.

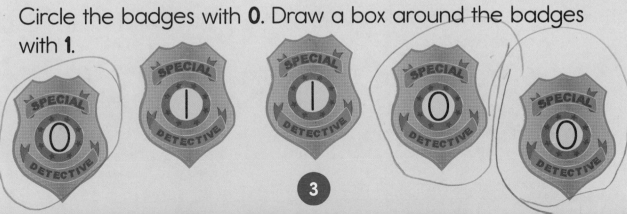

Add 2

Trace and write to solve the problems.

$0 + 2 =$

2

$1 + 2 =$

3

$+2$

$2 + 2 =$

4

$3 + 2 =$

5

Circle the pictures that go together.

Add 2

Trace and write to solve the problems.

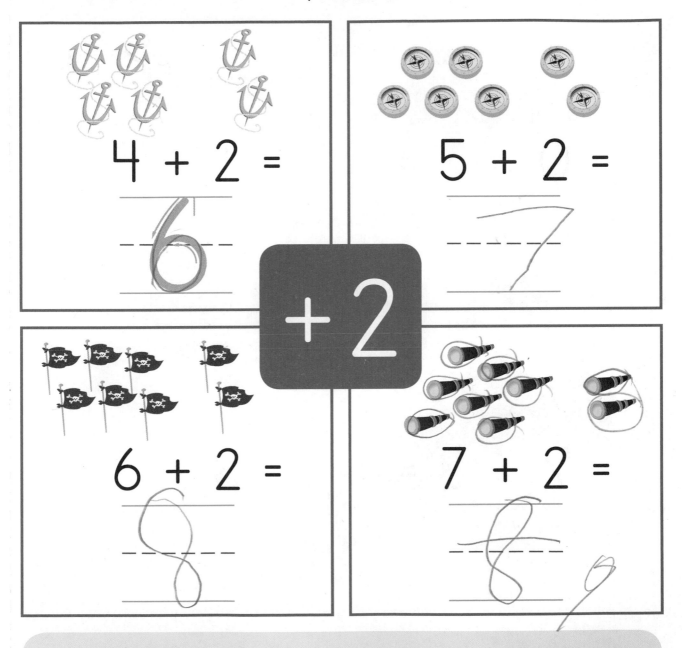

4 + 2 = 6

5 + 2 = 7

+2

6 + 2 = 8

7 + 2 = 8

Count the starfish. Circle the number.

0   1   2

Add 3

Trace and write to solve the problems.

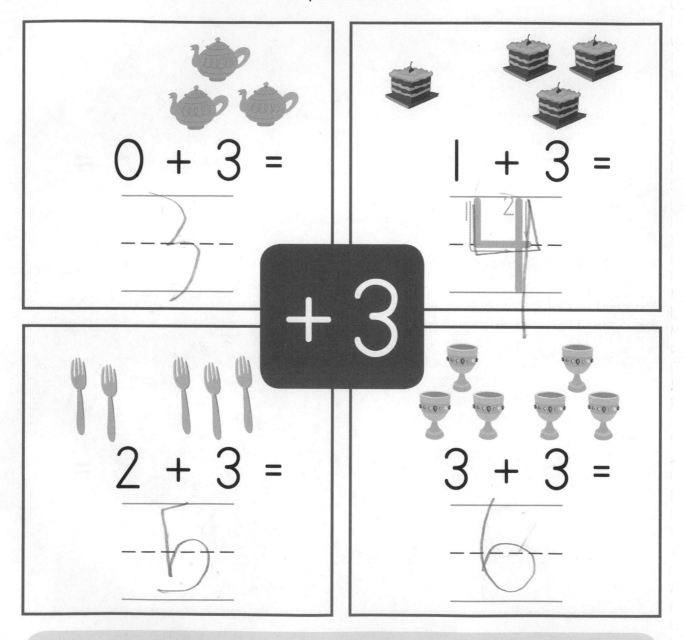

0 + 3 =

1 + 3 =

+3

2 + 3 =

3 + 3 =

Circle the trees that are taller. Draw an **X** on the trees that are shorter.

Add 3

Trace and write to solve the problems.

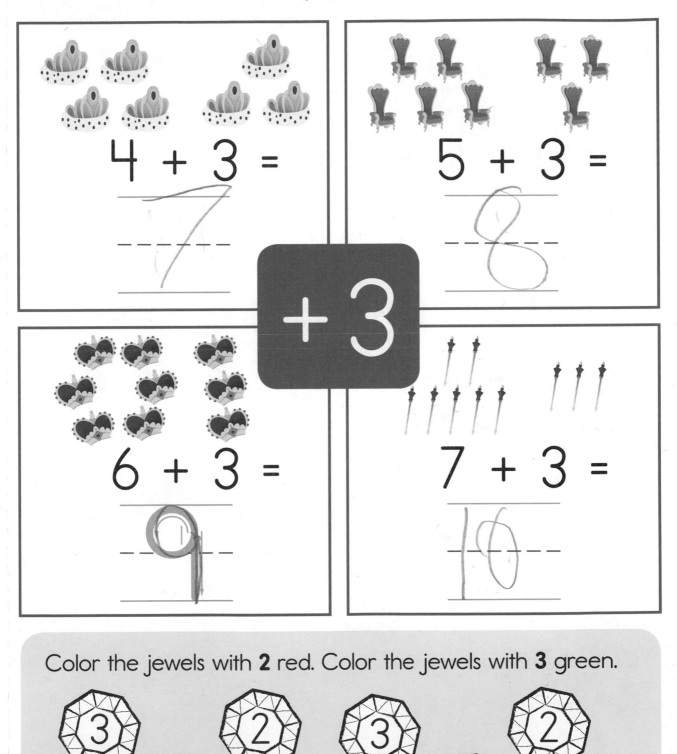

$4 + 3 =$ 7

$5 + 3 =$ 8

+3

$6 + 3 =$ 9

$7 + 3 =$ 10

Color the jewels with **2** red. Color the jewels with **3** green.

Add 4

Trace and write to solve the problems.

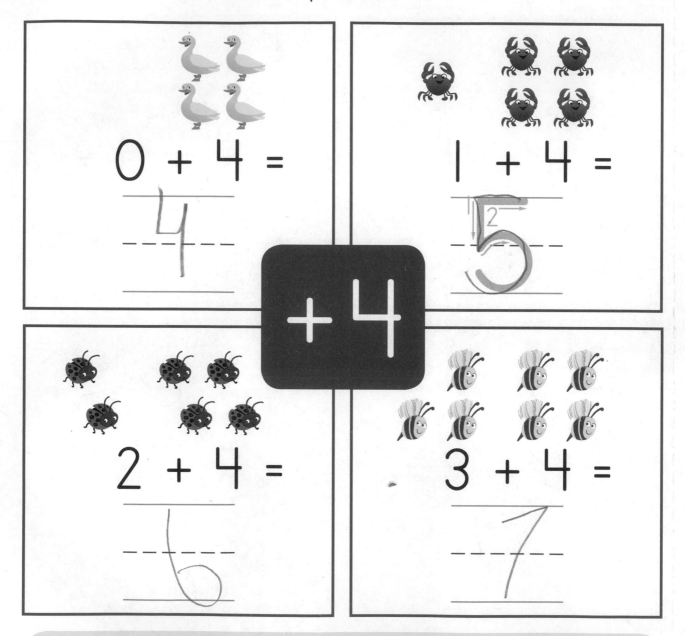

0 + 4 =

4

1 + 4 =

5

2 + 4 =

6

3 + 4 =

7

+4

Write the missing numbers.

1 _____ _____ 4

8

Add 4

Trace and write to solve the problems.

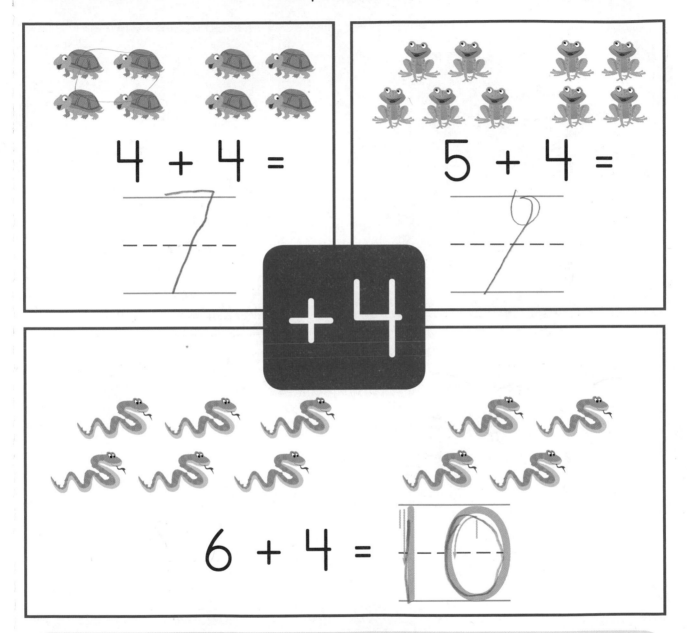

$4 + 4 =$ 7

$5 + 4 =$ 9

$+4$

$6 + 4 =$ 10

Draw **4** animals. Write the number.

_____

_ _ _ _ _ _

_____

Add 5

Trace and write to solve the problems.

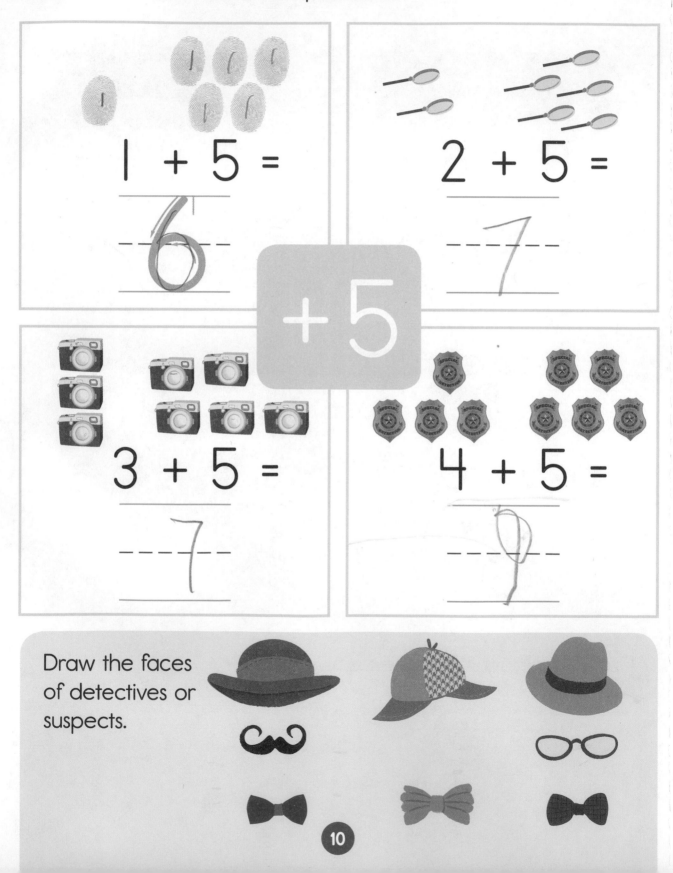

$1 + 5 =$

6

$2 + 5 =$

7

+5

$3 + 5 =$

7

$4 + 5 =$

9

Draw the faces of detectives or suspects.

Add 6

Trace and write to solve the problems.

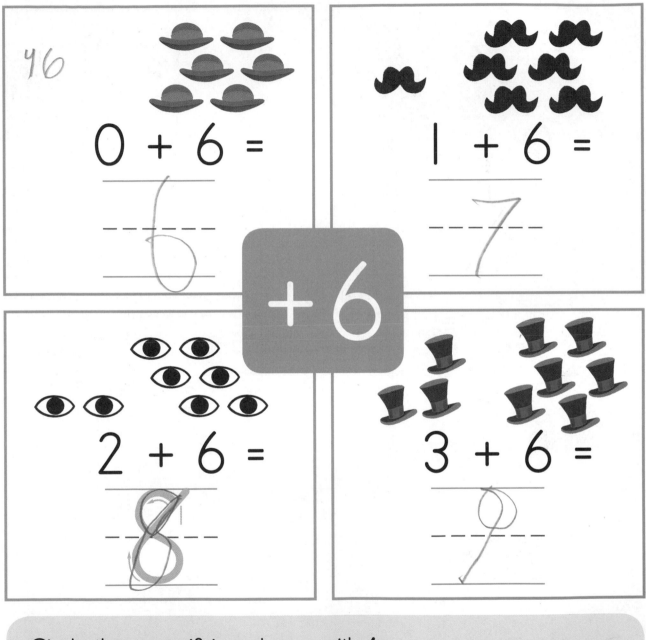

46

$0 + 6 =$

6

$1 + 6 =$

7

$+6$

$2 + 6 =$

8

$3 + 6 =$

9

Circle the magnifying glasses with **6**.

6   6   5   6   5

Add 7

Trace and write to solve the problems.

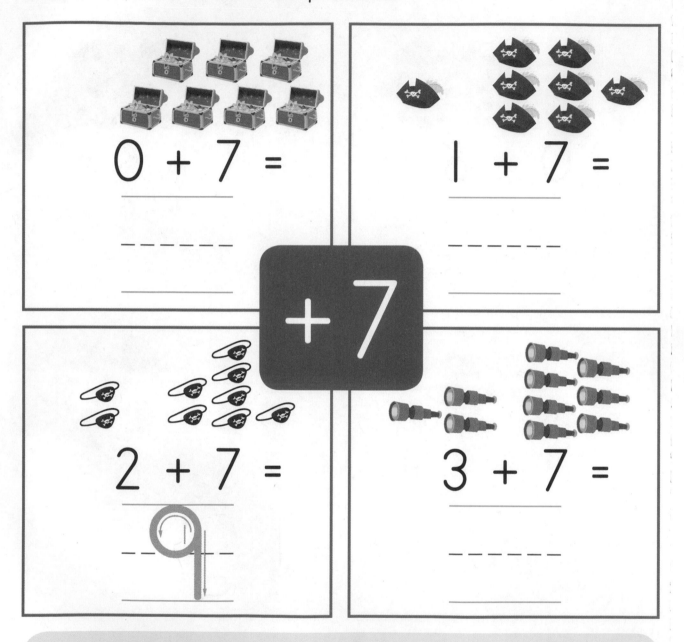

$0 + 7 =$

$1 + 7 =$

$+7$

$2 + 7 =$

9

$3 + 7 =$

Draw a jellyfish that is longer.

Add 8

Trace and write to solve the problems.

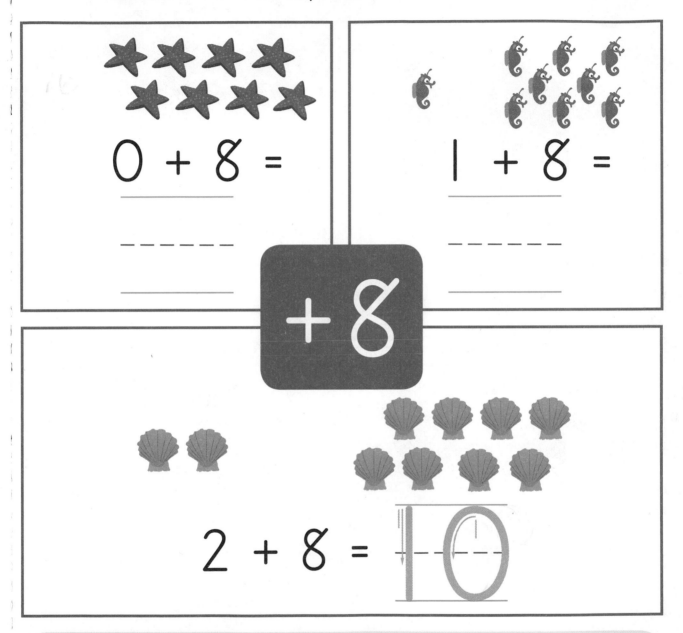

0 + 8 =

_____

- - - - - -

_____

1 + 8 =

_____

- - - - - -

_____

+8

2 + 8 = 10

Count the fish. Circle the number.

6 7 (8)

Add 9

Trace and write to solve the problems.

$0 + 9 =$ _____

$+9$

$1 + 9 =$ 10

Circle the monsters that are the same.

Make 10

Circle the number that completes each problem.

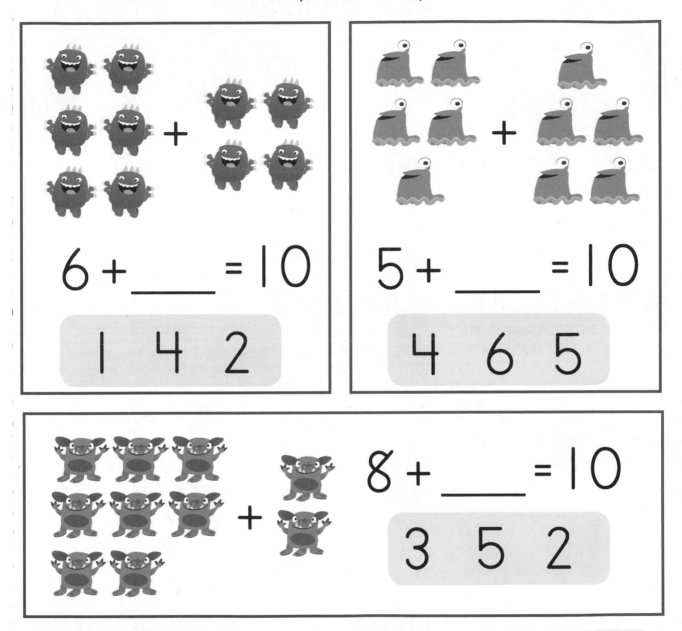

$6 +$ ___ $= 10$

1 4 2

$5 +$ ___ $= 10$

4 6 5

$8 +$ ___ $= 10$

3 5 2

Draw and color 10 monster eggs. Then, write the number.

_____

_ _ _ _ _ _

_____

I Know How to Add

Add. Use the pictures for help.

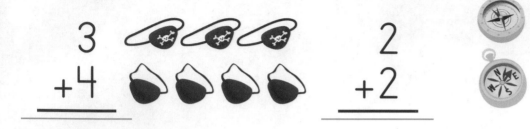

```
   3                    2
 + 4                  + 2
 ____                 ____

 _ _ _ _ _            _ _ _ _ _

 _____              _____
```

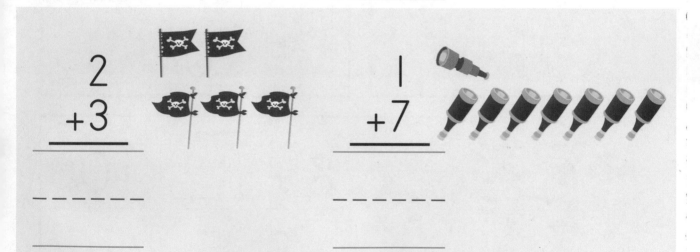

```
   2                    1
 + 3                  + 7
 ____                 ____

 _ _ _ _ _            _ _ _ _ _

 _____              _____
```

```
   5                    3
 + 5                  + 6
 ____                 ____

 _ _ _ _ _            _ _ _ _ _

 _____              _____
```

Subtract 0

Solve each problem. Then, trace or write the answer.

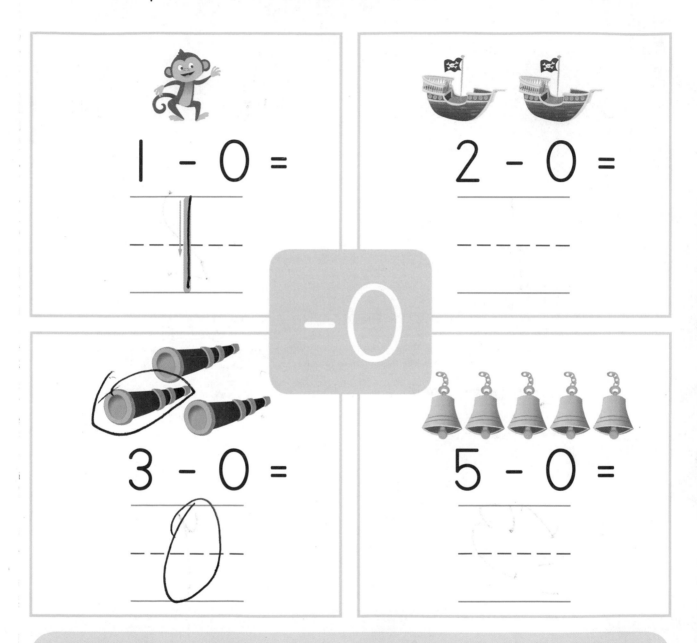

1 - 0 =

I

2 - 0 =

- - - - - -

3 - 0 =

O

5 - 0 =

- - - - - -

Count the crabs. Circle the number.

6   7   8

17

Subtract 1

Cross out an object to solve each problem. Then, trace or write the answer.

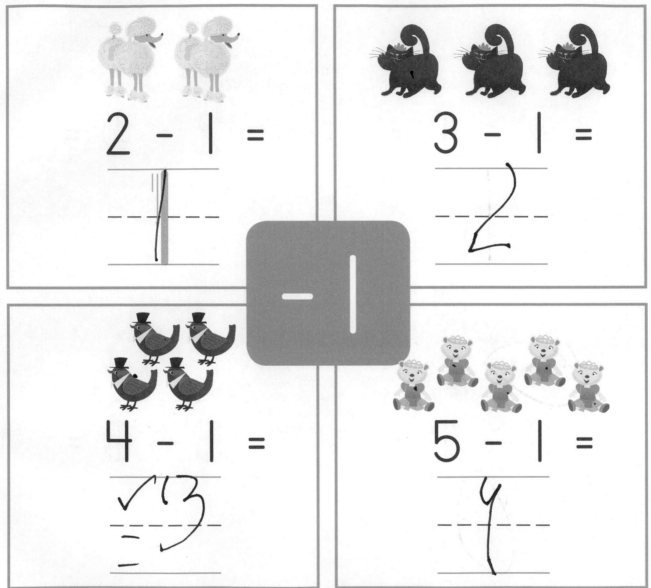

$2 - 1 =$ 1

$3 - 1 =$ 2

-1

$4 - 1 =$ 3

$5 - 1 =$ 4

Draw an **X** on the picture that does not belong.

Subtract 1

Cross out an object to solve each problem. Then, trace or write the answer.

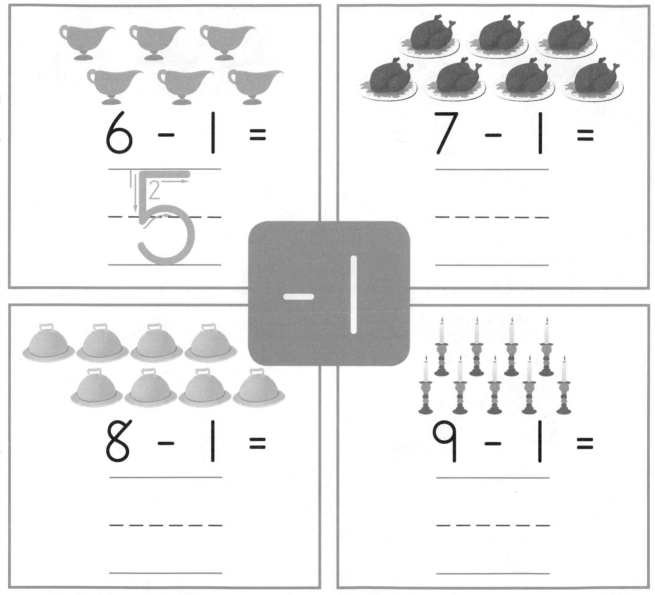

6 - 1 =

5

7 - 1 =

- 1

8 - 1 =

9 - 1 =

Count the thrones. Write the number.

Subtract 2

Cross out objects to solve each problem. Then, trace or write the answer.

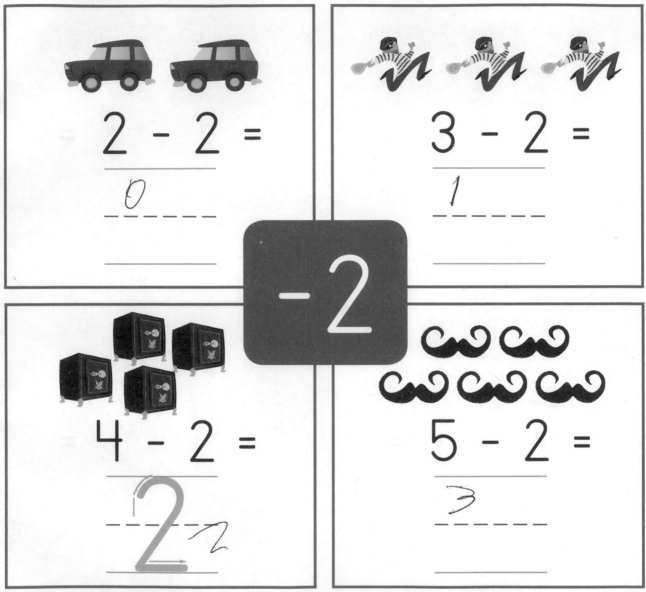

$2 - 2 =$

0

$3 - 2 =$

1

-2

$4 - 2 =$

2

$5 - 2 =$

3

Circle the fingerprint that is smaller. Draw an **X** on the fingerprint that is larger.

Subtract 2

Cross out objects to solve each problem. Then, trace or write the answer.

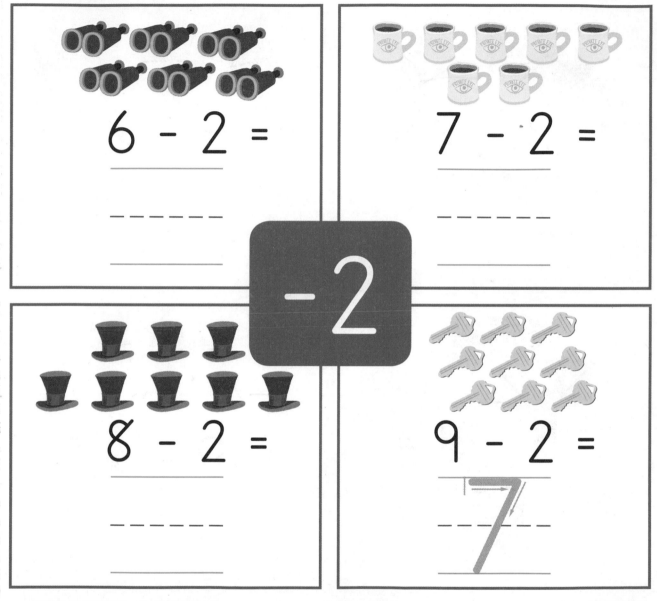

$6 - 2 =$

$7 - 2 =$

-2

$8 - 2 =$

$9 - 2 =$

7

Color **2** bats. Then, draw **2** more.

Subtract 3

Cross out objects to solve each problem. Then, trace or write the answer.

$3 - 3 =$

$4 - 3 =$

-3

$5 - 3 =$

$6 - 3 =$

Count the snakes. Then, draw an equal number of snakes.

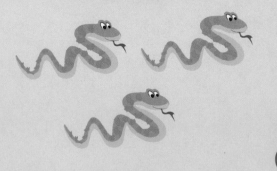

Subtract 3

Cross out objects to solve each problem. Then, trace or write the answer.

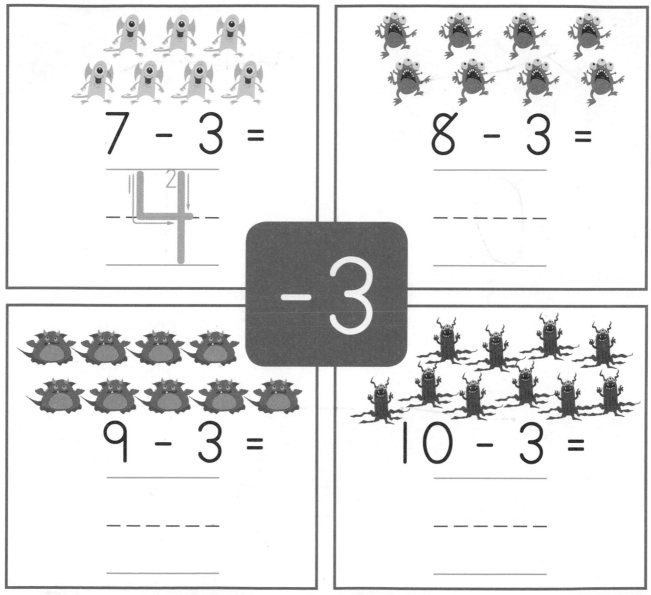

7 - 3 = 4

8 - 3 = _____

-3

9 - 3 = _____

10 - 3 = _____

Count the eyes on the monster. Circle the number.

2   3   4

Subtract 4

Cross out objects to solve each problem. Then, trace or write the answer.

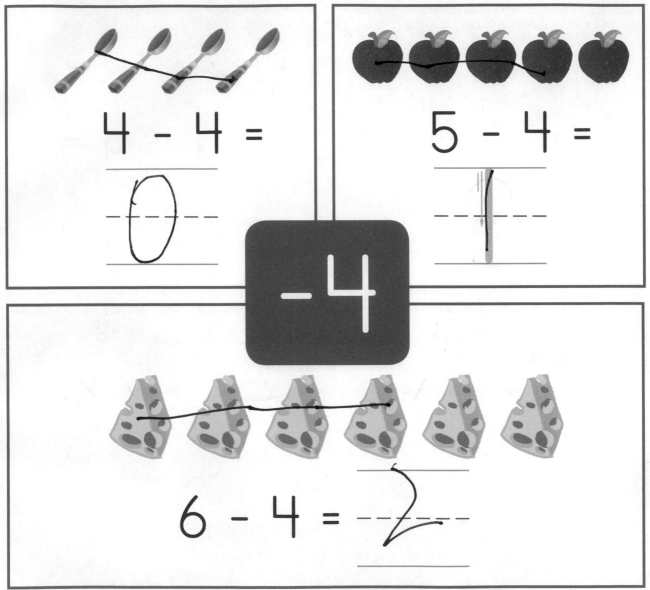

$4 - 4 = 0$

$5 - 4 = 1$

-4

$6 - 4 = 2$

Circle the group that has less.

24

Subtract 4

Cross out objects to solve each problem. Then, trace or write the answer.

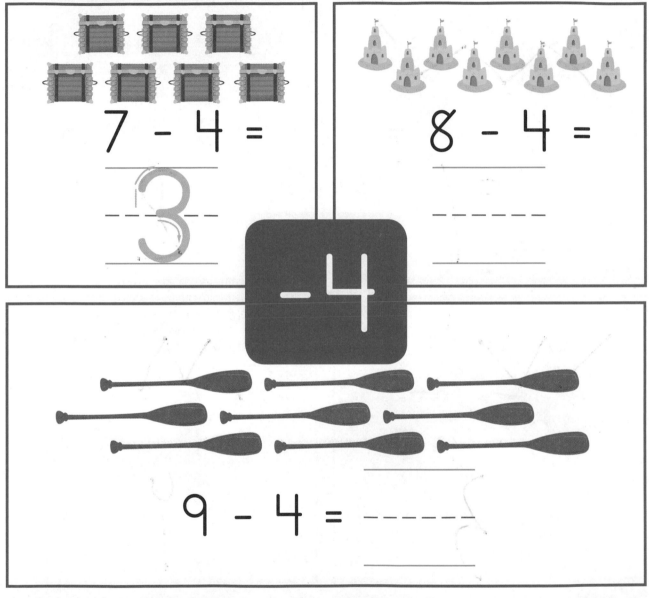

$7 - 4 =$

3

$8 - 4 =$

-4

$9 - 4 =$

Color each duck with **3** orange. Color each duck with **4** yellow.

Subtract 5

Cross out objects to solve each problem. Then, trace or write the answer.

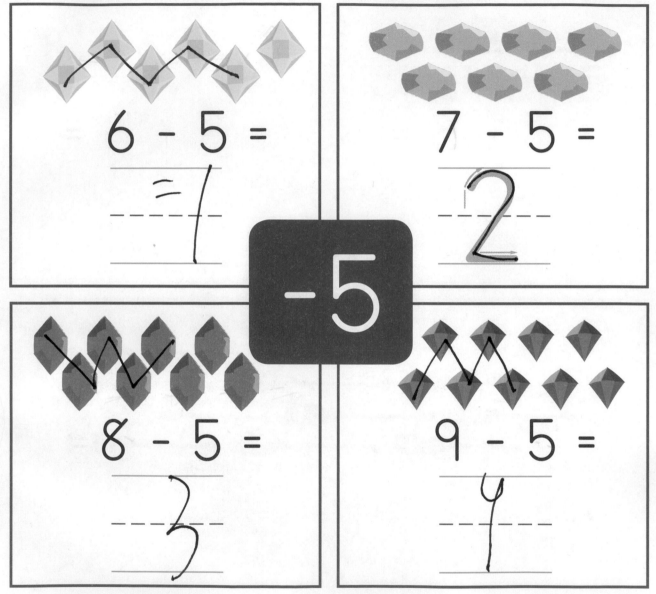

$6 - 5 =$ 1

$7 - 5 =$ 2

-5

$8 - 5 =$ 3

$9 - 5 =$ 4

Color the ball that comes next.

Subtract 6

Cross out objects to solve each problem. Then, trace or write the answer.

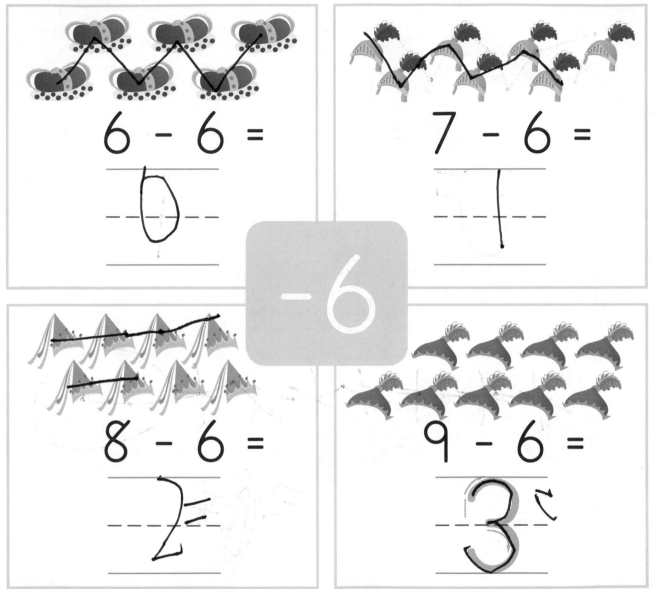

$6 - 6 = 0$

$7 - 6 = 1$

-6

$8 - 6 = 2$

$9 - 6 = 3$

Match the group of cups to the correct number.

6

8

9

Subtract 7

Cross out objects to solve each problem. Then, trace or write the answer.

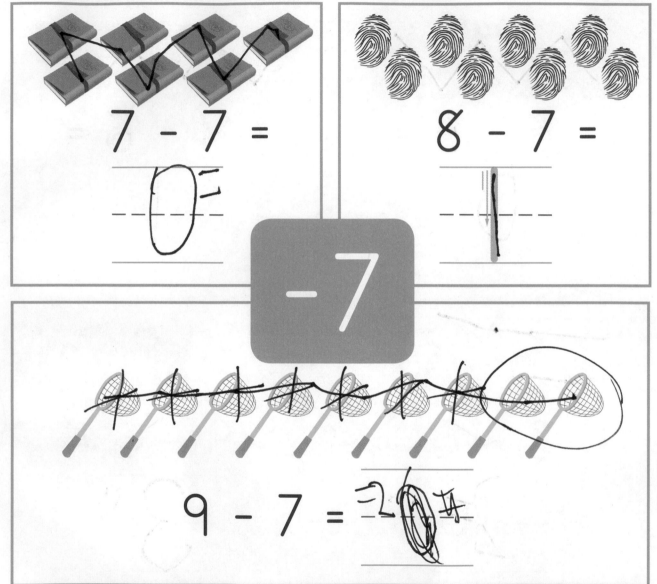

$7 - 7 =$

0

$8 - 7 =$

1

-7

$9 - 7 =$

Color the square blue. Color the rhombus purple.
Color the rectangle orange.

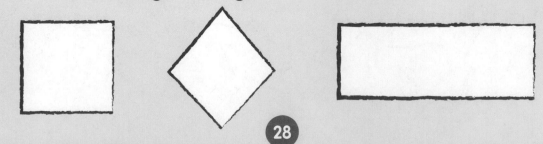

Subtract 8

Cross out objects to solve each problem. Then, trace or write the answer.

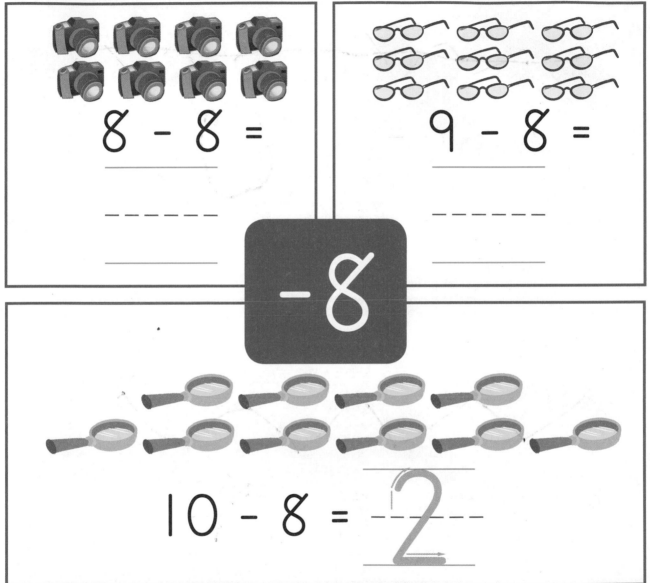

$8 - 8 =$

- - - - - - -

_____

$9 - 8 =$

- - - - - - -

_____

-8

$10 - 8 = 2$

Color the mittens with **8**.

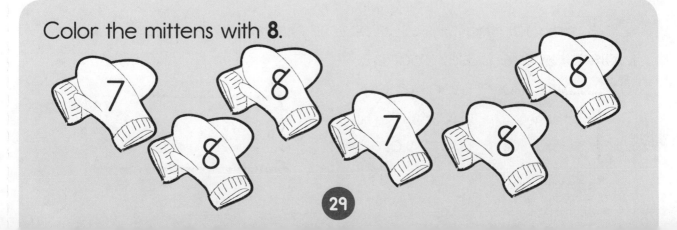

Subtract 9

Cross out objects to solve each problem. Then, trace or write the answer.

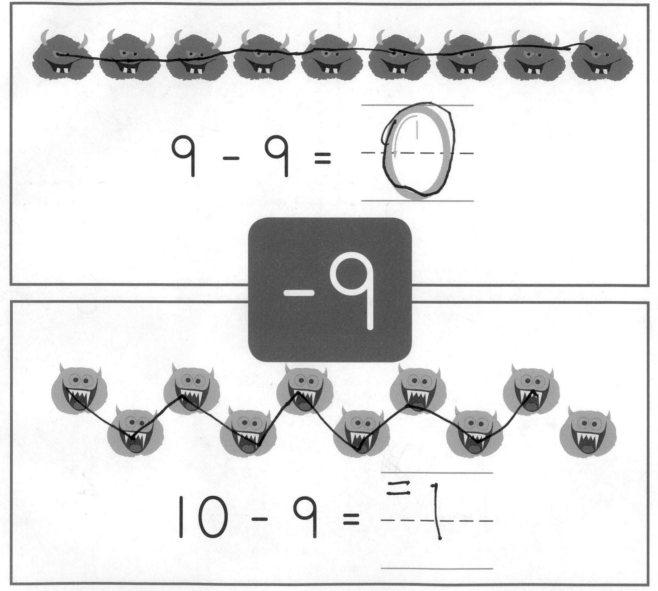

$$9 - 9 = 0$$

$$-9$$

$$10 - 9 = 1$$

One monster was waiting at the bus stop. Then, two more monsters came. Draw a picture. Write and solve a problem.

Subtract from 10

Count **10** monsters in each row. Cross out monsters to make the number shown.

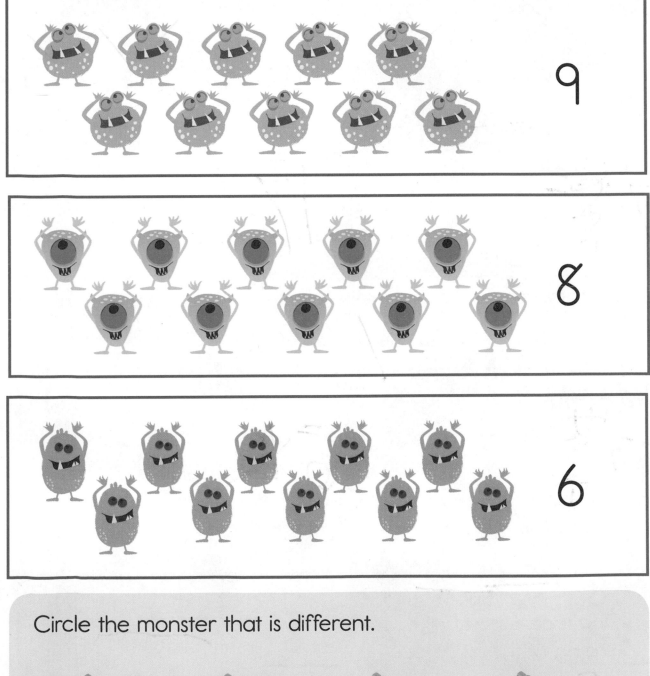

Circle the monster that is different.

I Know How to Subtract

Subtract. Count and cross out pictures to help.

7
−3
——
4

10
−7
——
7

4
−1
——
3

6
−4
——
6

8
−3
——
5

9
−8
——
8